What matters most of all to you?
What matters most to me?
Let's take a look around us,
and maybe we will see.

Is it being very big
or being super small?

Is it having lots of stuff
or not that much at all?

Is it talking all the time

or making time to hear?

Is it being really brave
or sometimes feeling fear?

Is it being in a crowd
or spending time alone?

Is it always going out

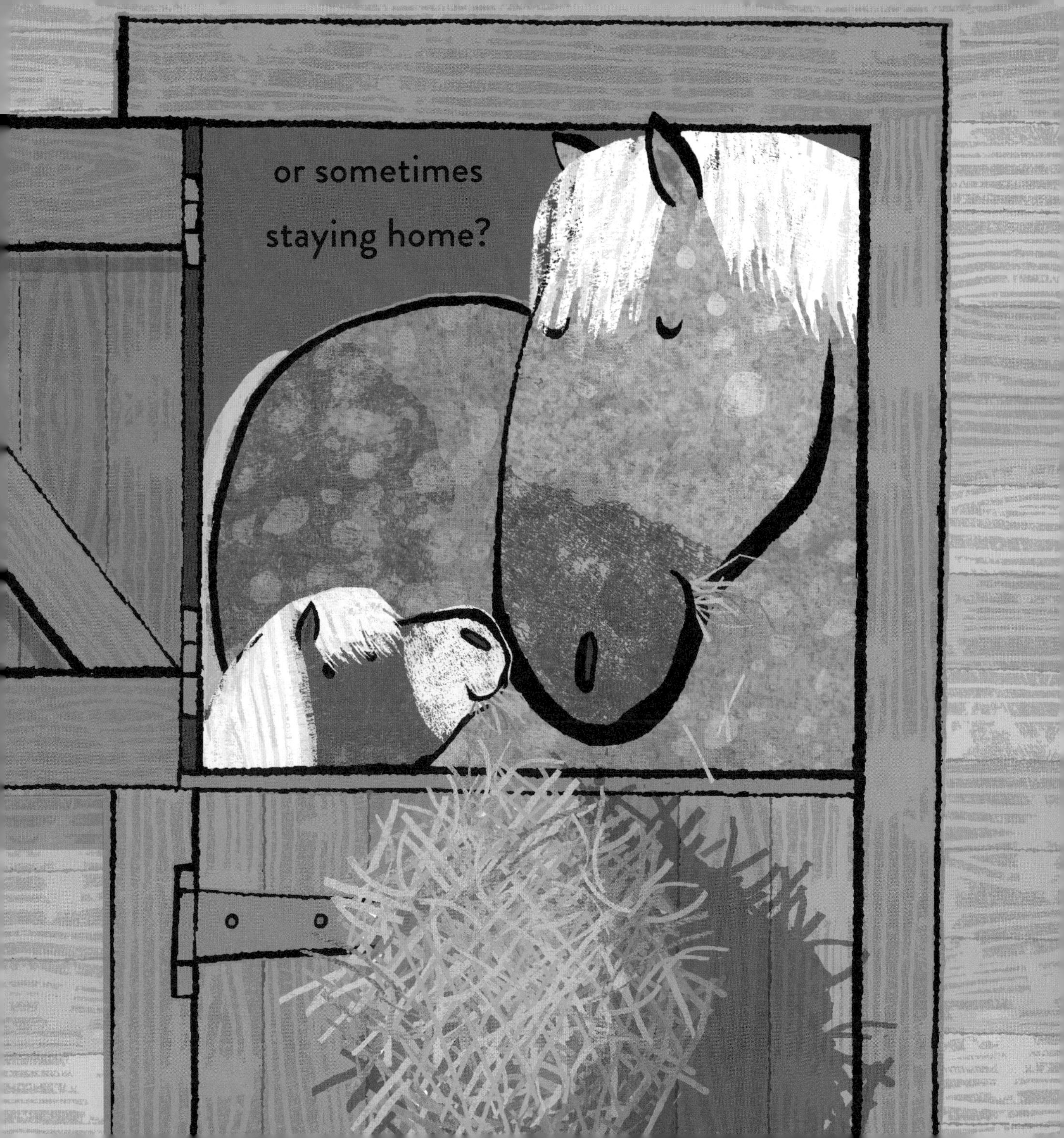
or sometimes
staying home?

Is it going very fast
or just taking it slow?

Is it knowing
everything,
or the things we
don't yet know?

Whether you are scared or brave,

or if you're big or small . . .

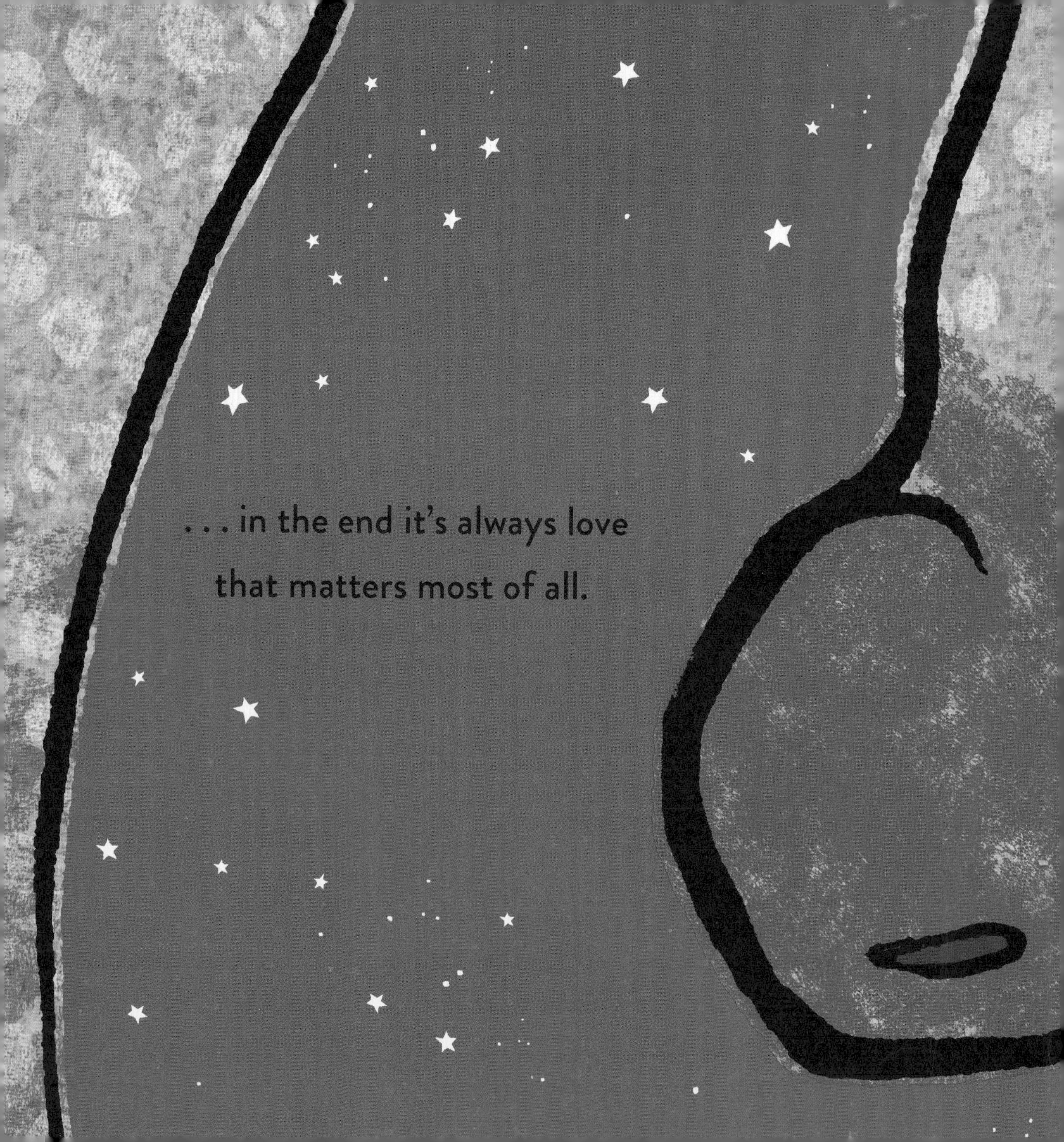

. . . in the end it's always love
that matters most of all.